This book is due for return on or before the last date shown below.

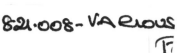
FULL FLIGHT

Contents

Badger Publishing

Temper Temper

He kicked it, he smacked it,
he got a stick and whacked it,
but no-matter how much he attacked it,
he couldn't make it move.

He pulled at it, he tore at it,
he shouted and he swore at it,
but no-matter how much he got sore at it,
he couldn't make it move.

So Dad left his car at the shops,
caught the bus home,
and was mean to us for the rest of the day.

Mike Jubb

Michael Owen

Michael Owen, Michael Owen
Runs so fast his pants are showing
Kicks the ball for all his worth
Now it's orbiting the Earth.

Roger Stevens

A Footballer's Prayer

Dear God
Please bless my feet
May they kick a ball
Real sweet!
Keep my balance
Keep me on my toes
Help my team mates
Outfox my foes
May my feet
Lead me to victory
Win the match and win the double
And may my feet always
Walk away from trouble.

Roger Stevens

Where's Grandma?

Ever since my little brother
Buried Granddad on the beach,
We've had to keep Grandma
Out of reach.

We hid her in the attic
But he very nearly had her
When he poked her with his spade
After climbing up the ladder.

Ever since my little brother
Buried Granddad in the sand,
Grandma's been complaining he's
Out of hand.

It's just a phase, my mother said,
My brother will soon chuck it,
But the last we saw of Grandma
Was my brother's empty bucket.

Celia Warren

This Kid

There's this kid, right,
Who I hate with all my might.
A revolting chap,
Who wears a baseball cap,
And is built of medium height

What really gets me
Is his voice see.
Squeaky and squawky,
High pitched and dorky,
It just drives everyone barmy.

The noise of his vowels
Twists my face in scowls
His nouns and verbs
Annoy and disturb
They're like cats attacking owls.

So if he's making a sound
When I'm hanging around,
Or if I hear him talk,
When I'm out for a walk,
I'll ask him to shut up for a pound.

Ivor Baddiel

I'd Love to Play for Man United

I'd love to play for Man United
Before each game I'd get excited
Pull my shirt on, full of pride
Down the tunnel with my side.

I'd love to play for Man United
It would make me so delighted
On the pitch before the game
Hear the crowd all chant my name.

I'd love to play for Man United
See the ball so smoothly flighted
Running in my striker's role
Whack the ball into the goal.

I'd love to play for Man United
It would be like being knighted
But maybe it's all just a dream
Perhaps I'll start with my school team.

Jonny Zucker

If You've Got To Fall

If you've got to fall,
don't fall on your back,
don't land on your arm
and give it a crack.

Don't twist your ankle,
don't crash to your knees,
don't flatten your nose
when you jump from a tree.

Don't fracture your wrist
or give elbows a clout,
don't bend back your fingers
or knock yourself out.

Don't fall on your face,
don't fall on your tum.
If you've got to fall,
then fall on your... best friend!

Brian Moses

City Sounds Heard After Dark

The sweesh sweesh of speeding cars.
Old songs from the crowded bars.
Disco drums and loud guitars.

Aircraft zapping through the sky.
Rooftop cats that spit and cry.
Laughter from the passer-by.

Motorbikers' sudden roar.
Corner lads who josh and jaw.
A call. A shout. A slammed door.

The guard dogs that howl and bark.
Voices from the padlocked park.
City sounds heard after dark.

Wes Magee

How to score with the public

I'm a famous footballer
The girls all think I'm great,
I'm married to a pop star,
The prime minister's a mate.

They've given me a chat show,
And millions tune in,
The whole nation's bought my poster
They just love my cheesy grin.

My haircut hits the headlines,
I've grown designer stubble;
But I've given up the football -
Real work's just too much trouble.

David Orme

School Photo

Here we go, the same old game:
Can I escape the photo frame?

Mum's got out her broken comb:
I wish, I wish, she'd stayed at home!

Now her hankie and some spit!
I'm out of here! And that... is... IT!

Six weeks later friends collect
Their pretty portraits. I forget.

Mum sees my teacher. Has a word.
Discovers that my photo's blurred.

I smile and sigh with great relief.
I'm saved from this year's mantelpiece!

Celia Warren

The New Teacher

He tried to be funny.
He cracked a few jokes.
But he looked scared
To me.

He told us he was strict.
He did that long silence.
The I Can Wait As Long As You thing.
But when Des burped
He lost it - and shouted.

He's obviously quite bright.
He can rattle off his seven times table.
No problem.

He tells an interesting story.
It was a shame Fiona fidgeted
And had to be sent to the Head Teacher's office.

I quite like him.

Roger Stevens

The Overtaker

I'm an overtaker,
straight down the line,
I don't hang about,
I haven't got time.

I'm an overtaker,
I can't stay back,
out in front,
ahead of the pack.

Better keep clear
in the swimming bath,
everybody
out of my path.

I'm an overtaker,
watch me run,
every sports day,
sound of the gun.

There I go,
off down the track,
nothing is going to hold me back.

If there's a record
I'm out to beat it,
record breakers
watch me defeat it.

Head in the clouds,
I don't look round,
keep my feet
clear of the ground.

I'm an overtaker,
any old race,
in an eating contest
I'd be in first place.

Run to school,
scoot home at night,
any distance
that's alright.

Hundred metres,
second to none,
I'm an overtaker,
watch me rrrrrrr.............un!

Brian Moses

Mates

When I took my ball to the park yesterday
I met a kid who said we could be mates.
We played footy, me and my mate.

Then my mate's friend and
his friend's pal turned up.
So we all played footy with my ball.

We played two a side.
Me and my mate versus
my mate's friend and my mate's friend's pal.

Me and my mate were winning 6-5 when
my mate's friend's pal kicked the ball
right over the wall into an old man's garden.

Then my mate's friend
and my mate's friend's pal
said they had to go home.

And my mate said he didn't want
to be my mate any more.
So I fetched my ball
and went home.

Mike Jubb

The Bully

The Bully talks tough
His voice scars and grates
Corners his prey
With the help of his mates.

Uses his words
To hassle and scare
Pushes you down
When there's nobody there.

Lurks in the hallways
To wander and roam
Stands in your way
When you're on your way home.

Why does he do it?
What's on his mind?
What makes him nasty?
Cruel and unkind?

He might stop at nothing
So be always prepared
'Cos inside every Bully
Is a person who's scared.

Jonny Zucker

When Beckham...

When Beckham passed,
The crowd gasped.
When Beckham back heeled,
The crowd squealed.
When Beckham tackled,
The crowd cackled.
When Beckham was fouled,
The crowd growled.
When Beckham missed,
The crowd hissed.
But when Beckham scored,
The crowd roared.

And roared, and roared and roared.

Ivor Baddiel

I Like Emma

I like Emma
but I don't know
if she likes me.
All the boys
think I'm a fool.

I wait outside the school gate
at half past three
trying to keep my cool.
Emma walks past,
shaking her blond hair free,
laughs with her friends
and drifts off home for tea.

Emma's two years
older than me.
Her class is higher
up the school.

I like Emma
but I don't know
if she likes me.
All the boys
think I'm a fool.

Wes Magee

Tyrannosaurus Chicken

They say
I'm just a chicken.

They use my name
for cowards:

"You're chicken!"
They shout.

But I've just found out
Something really exciting.

The chicken on the next perch
Said, "Guess what!

WE ARE DESCENDED FROM DINOSAURS!"

I'm looking forward to when
The bloke who collects the eggs come round.

We've got it all planned.
He's going to get

The biggest shock
Of his life!

David Orme

School Tie

The school rules state clearly
School tie must be worn
In the correct manner
It's the school uniform.

So we all wore it short
Half way up our chests
Then loose like a scarf
I liked that way best.

For a few days we tied the knot
Tight as we dare
Until Darren fainted.
And fell off his chair.

A fat knot in spring
As thick as your head
In summer we unpicked it
As thin as a thread.

None of us wore it
How the tie should be worn
'cos we're all individuals
And we don't conform.

Roger Stevens

The Soccer Star

FOOTBALL CROWD GOES CRAZY
Picture on page one:
Shorts round Scorer's ankles -
Tie-string came undone!

CAPTAIN'S HAPLESS HAT-TRICK
Details on page eight:
Captain scored three easy goals -
Own goal, he learnt too late!

GOALIE HEAD-BUTTS GOAL-POST
Turn to centre page:
Someone broke his daisy-chain -
Put him in a rage!

SUPER-GLUE DISASTER
Feature on page three:
Player's toecap sticks to ball -
Replay planned next week.

PENALTY CALAMITY
See page seventeen:
Defender disappears with ball -
Nowhere to be seen!

Celia Warren

The Slow Toad and the Fast Car

Old toad,
cold and warty,
creeps across the road,
couldn't give a toss
about left and right.

New car,
hot-headed
and sporty-red;
speeding eyes in the night.

Old toad
makes it to the middle.
New car
shakes the air,
doesn't care.

Old toad,
really a witch.
New car,
in the ditch.

Mike Jubb

Your Passing Was Rubbish

You're the worst, he said, as he slammed shut the door,
Your passing was rubbish, your shooting was poor!
Our coach Mr. Gray was angry with us.
We'd just lost ten nil, he was making a fuss.
You stood still like lemons and they ran so fast.
You moved like small snails and let them go past.
His face looked all hot as he ranted and hissed.
He pointed his fingers and banged down his fist.
You missed all your tackles as they scored more goals.
The defence was so bad it was filled with great holes.
He scratched his head, he slapped his knee.
And I felt that he was looking at me.
You didn't move, you didn't pass.
You looked like cows all eating grass.
Did we do anything *right?* The team all chime.
You turned up for the game on time.

Jonny Zucker

How Can I?

How can I wind up my brother
when I haven't got the key?

How can I turn on my charm
when I can't even find the switch?

How can I snap at my mother
when I'm not a crocodile?

How can I stir up my sister
when I'm not even holding a spoon?

How can I pick up my feet
and not fall to the ground on my knees?

How can I stretch my legs
when they're long enough already?

Parents! - They ask the impossible!

Brian Moses

I Have a Wicked Granny

I have a wicked granny
with a wicked kind of grin
that twitches the wrinkles
on her wicked little chin.
She tells wicked stories
that always begin
I have a wicked granny
with a wicked kind of grin.

Celia Warren

Ten:Nil

The phantom fans are chanting.
There's a cheer in my ear as I score.
I've done it again: ten goals to me
And nil to the garage door!

Celia Warren

A Wolf Came Through
My Bedroom Door

"A wolf came through my bedroom door,
His paws pad-padding on the floor.

I felt his hot breath in my face,
It seemed so real,
It seemed he was really there.

The wolves came through my bedroom wall
My muscles couldn't move at all.

Their heads were huge,
Red eyes, hungry, teeth dribbling,
Great hungry teeth...

Then I woke up. And that was that."

So why are there paw prints on your mat?

David Orme

27

Miss Jones, Football Teacher

Miss Jones
    football teacher
red shellsuit
    flash boots.
She laughs
    as she dribbles,
shrieks, 'GOAL!'
    when she
       shoots.

Miss Jones
    what a creature
pink lipstick
    shin pads.
See there
    on the touchline
lines of drooling
    lads.

Miss Jones'
    finest feature
long blonde hair
    - it's neat!
She 'bend' kicks
    and back-heels,
she's fast on her
    feet.

Miss Jones
    football teacher
told us, 'Don't
    give up!'
She made us
    train harder,
and we won
    the Cup!

Wes Magee

Limericks

There once was a young lad on skates
Who thought his skill would win him dates
But he fell when he turned
And all that he earned
Was some laughter from all of his mates

A long haired girl wanted more powers
To speed up the time after showers
Her brother's cropped quiff
Could be dried in a jiff
While she used a dryer for hours.

There once was a teacher from space
Whose lessons went at a mad pace
He ate weird-looking breads
And he had seven heads
So you never knew which one to face.

Jonny Zucker

My Brother Said

My brother said, 'I'll flatten you,
I'll tip you off your feet,
I'll push your teeth to the back of your head,
I'll knock you from here to next week.
I'll sort you out, I'll destroy your face,
when I've finished, you won't even look
as if you belong to the human race!
I'll really give you a hiding,
I'll clobber you, I'll make you wail.
I'm going to make you regret it,
your face will really turn pale.
I'll hammer you, I'll rattle your bones,
I'll fill you full of dread.'
And I only told his girlfriend
that he still takes his teddy to bed!

Brian Moses

Star Wars Day

May 4th

On Star Wars Day
Be brave and true
May the Fourth
Be with you

Roger Stevens

Never Trust A Lemon

Never trust a lemon -
It's a melon in disguise.
Never trust potatoes
With shifty eyes.
Never trust a radish -
It repeats all that it hears.
Never trust an onion.
It will all end in tears.

Roger Stevens

Titles in Full Flight

Badger Publishing Limited
26 Wedgwood Way, Pin Green Industrial Estate, Stevenage, Herts. SG1 4QF
Telephone: 01438 356907. Fax: 01438 747015.
www.badger-publishing.co.uk   enquiries@badger-publishing.co.uk

Your Passing Was Rubbish and other poems   ISBN 1 85880 929 0

Editing, series editing and poems I'd Love To Play for Man United, The Bully, Your Passing Was Rubbish and Limericks © Jonny Zucker 2002. Complete work © Badger Publishing Limited 2002. Poems. This Kid, When Beckham... © Ivor Baddiel 2002. Temper temper, Mates, The Slow Toad and the Fast Car © Mike Jubb 2002. City Sounds Heard After Dark, I Like Emma, Miss Jones Football Teacher © Wes Magee 2002. If You've Got To Fall, The Overtaker, How Can I?, My Brother Said © Brian Moses 2002. How to score with the public, Tyrannosaurus Chicken, A wolf came through my bedroom door © David Orme 2002. Michael Owen, A Footballer's Prayer, The New Teacher, School Tie, Star Wars Day, Never Trust A Lemon © Roger Stevens 2002. Where's Grandma?, School Photo, The Soccer Star, I Have a Wicked Granny and Ten:Nil (first published in *They Think It's All Over* ed. David Orme, Macmillan, 1998) © Celia Warren 2002.

Series Editor: Jonny Zucker.   Editor: Paul Martin.
Cover design: Jain Birchenough.   Cover illustration: Paul Savage.
Publisher: David Jamieson.

Printed and bound in China through Colorcraft Ltd., Hong Kong